Enrichment Book

Ann Moran
Anne and Leonard Frobisher

gill & macmillan primary

Gill & Macmillan
Hume Avenue
Park West
Dublin 12
www.gillmacmillan.ie

ISBN: 978 07171 53800

© Ann Moran, Anne and Leonard Frobisher 2014

Design: Design Image
Print origination: Carole Lynch
Internal illustrations: Kate Shannon and Sting Art
Technical drawings: MPS Limited
Cover illustration: www.designbos.ie
Consultant editor in mathematics curriculum and pedagogy: Betty Stoutt

The paper used in this book comes from the wood pulp of
managed forests. For every tree felled, at least one tree is
planted, thereby renewing natural resources.

Any links to external websites should not be construed as an endorsement
by Gill & Macmillan of the content or view of the linked material.
Equations on pages 2, 5, 8, 11, 14, 18, 22, 26, 29, 32, 35, 38, 41, 44, 48, 51, 54, 57, 60, 63, 67,
70, 73, 76, 79, 82, 85, 88, 91, originally published by Macmillan Education Australia.
Copyright Peter Maher/Macmillan Education Australia 2011 Macmillan Maths Problem
Solving Box 1 ISBN: 9781420293937

The publishers have made every effort to contact copyright holders
but any omissions will be rectified at the next reprint.

Unit	Strand	Page
1. Look Back		
2. Place Value	Number	1
3. Addition	Number	4
4. Subtraction	Number	7
5. Chance	Data	10
6. Multiplication 1	Number	13
7. Division 1	Number	16
8. Check-up 1	Revision	*
9. Fractions 1	Number	20
10. Multiplication 2	Number	24
11. Length	Measures	28
12. Division 2	Number	31
13. Number Patterns and Sequences	Algebra	34
14. Check-up 2	Revision	*
15. Multiplication 3	Number	37
16. Division 3	Number	40
17. Fractions 2	Number	43
18. Decimals	Number	46
19. Check-up 3	Revision	*
20. Area	Measures	50
21. Money	Measures	53
22. Symmetry	Shape and Space	56
23. Multiplication 4	Number	59
24. 2-D Shapes	Shape and Space	62

25.	Division 4	Number	65
26.	Time I	Measures	69
27.	Check-up 4	Revision	*
28.	Lines and Angles	Shape and Space	72
29.	Weight	Measures	75
30.	Number Sentences	Algebra	78
31.	Representing and Interpreting Data	Data	81
32.	Time 2	Measures	84
33.	3-D Shapes	Shape and Space	87
34.	Capacity	Measures	90
35.	Check-up 5	Revision	*

*Access all Check-ups on our website, www.crackingmaths.ie

1. Write the numbers represented on these notation boards.

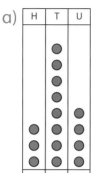 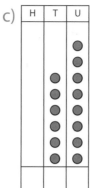 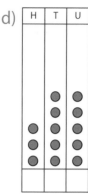

2. Complete these notation boards in your copy.

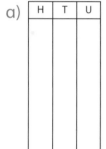  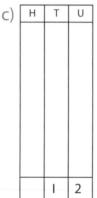  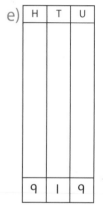

3. Draw abacuses in your copy to show the following numbers.
   a) 749   b) 910   c) 100   d) 99

4. Write the following numbers in words in your copy.
   a) 300   b) 462   c) 802   d) 480

5. Write the following numbers in digits in your copy.
   a) One hundred and twenty-one   b) Fifty-seven
   c) Two hundred and twenty-two   d) Seven hundred and seven

6. Write the following numbers in expanded form.
   For example: 842 = 8 hundreds + 4 tens + 2 units OR 800 + 40 + 2
   a) 312   b) 650   c) 67   d) 489

7. a) Draw the number line and fill in these numbers on it:
247, 251, 257 and 249.

250   255

b) Now write the four numbers in order, from smallest to largest.

8. Write down the value of the underlined digit in the following numbers.

a) 5̲45   b) 1̲1̲2   c) 80̲6

9. Round these numbers to the nearest ten.

a) 89   b) 42   c) 11   d) 16   e) 75   f) 97

10. Round these numbers to the nearest hundred.

a) 387   b) 514   c) 817   d) 221   e) 869   f) 49

11. Write the following number in expanded form in your copy.

385.4 = ___ hundreds + ___ tens + ___ units + ___ tenths
OR ___ + ___ + ___ + ___

Solve!   2. Place Value

· ·

2-digit Numbers

Find the 3rd biggest 2-digit number.

Now find the smallest 2-digit number.

Take the smaller number away from the bigger number. What is left over?

Strategy hints!

1. Look for the important words in the question.

2. Think logically.

Extension

Take away the 2nd smallest 2-digit number from the 2nd biggest 2-digit number. What do you notice?

1. Making 3-digit Numbers

Nathan has 4 digit cards.

| 0 | 1 | 2 | 3 |

hundreds	tens	units
3	0	1

He uses 3 of his cards to make a 3-digit number in his place value chart.

Make a copy of what Nathan did.

Nathan says, 'I have made the number three hundred and one.'

Is what Nathan said correct?

Explain why to a friend.

> Investigate other 3-digit numbers Nathan could make with his digit cards.

2. Rounding

Grace has two 3-digit numbers to round in different ways.

273 rounded to the nearest 10 is ☐

273 rounded to the nearest 100 is ☐

489 rounded to the nearest 10 is ☐

489 rounded to the nearest 100 is ☐

Work out the answers for Grace.

Explain to a friend how you worked them out.

Grace says, 'My roundings of 273 and 489 show that every 3-digit number is greater when rounded to the nearest hundred than when rounded to the nearest ten.'

Explain to a friend what Grace means.

> Investigate Grace's statement for other 3-digit numbers.

1. a)   23   b)   75   c)   266   d)   141

    + 74   + 25   + 87   + 299

2. Rewrite these downwards in your copy and solve.

   a) $19 + 30$ b) $854 + 19$

3. Try these.

   a) H T U   b) H T U   c) H T U   d) H T U

       1 2 3   7 0 1   8 7 7   4 6 0

    + 4 7 1   + 6 5 6   + 1 0 8   +   5 2

   e) H T U   f) H T U   g) H T U

       1 9 9   5 8 7   8 5 0

    + 2 5 0   + 2 2 2   + 1 4 9

4. Rewrite these downwards in your copy and solve.

   a) $420 + 62$ b) $246 + 135$

   c) $202 + 416 + 111$ d) $741 + 52 + 3$

5. a) H T U   b) H T U   c) H T U   d) H T U   e) H T U

       5 0 5   5 5 5   9 9   1 2 5   3 8 7

       1 0 1   3 0   2 8 8   6   2 6 0

    + 2 0 2   + 1 1   +3 4 1   + 6 2 4   + 9 9

6. Estimate the answers.

   a) $197 + 28$ b) $302 + 205$ c) $91 + 19$

7. Katie and her Uncle Peter were spending a day together visiting art galleries in Dublin. They looked at 74 paintings in the National Gallery, 29 paintings in the Hugh Lane Gallery and 60 paintings and 12 sculptures in the Museum of Modern Art. How many pieces of art did Katie and her Uncle Peter see altogether that day?

Solve!   3. Addition

Halfway Through

a) I open up my book.

I have just read page 30.

I see that I am halfway through the book.

How many pages are in the book?

b) My brother is also halfway through his book.
He is on page 52.

How many pages are in his book?

Extension

I open up a different book.

I have just read page 20.

I see that I am 6 pages away from having read half of the book.

How many pages are in the book?

Strategy hints!

1. Look for the important words in the question.
2. Have a go.
3. Think logically.

1. P Is for Palindrome

Amy says, '62 is not a palindromic number. But the answer to this addition is. 62 has a p value of 1.'

Make a copy of Amy's addition.

$$\begin{array}{r} 6\ 2 \\ +\ 2\ 6 \\ \hline 8\ 8 \end{array}$$

Amy then says, '39 is not a palindromic number. But the answer to this addition is. 39 has a p value of 2.'

Make a copy of what Amy did.

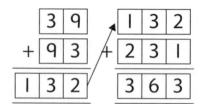

Investigate p values of 2-digit numbers less than 60.

2. A Consecutive 5

Michael makes the first 3 additions in a sequence of additions.

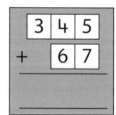

Complete the answers for Michael.

Extend the sequence of additions.

Explain when and why the sequence comes to an end to a friend.

Investigate patterns in the additions and their answers.

1. a) $\begin{array}{r} 78 \\ -\ 25 \\ \hline \end{array}$ b) $\begin{array}{r} 45 \\ -\ 3 \\ \hline \end{array}$ c) $\begin{array}{r} 187 \\ -\ 78 \\ \hline \end{array}$ d) $\begin{array}{r} 301 \\ -\ 281 \\ \hline \end{array}$

2. Rewrite these downwards in your copy and solve.

    a) 44 – 19   b) 811 – 422

3. Ciara has 68 apps downloaded to her mobile phone. If she deletes 29 of them, how many apps has she left on her phone?

4. Try these.

    a) H T U
       5 8 0
    –   2 0

    b) H T U
       2 0 7
    –   2 2

    c) H T U
       6 7 2
    – 1 0 9

    d) H T U
       5 1 3
    –   6 6

    e) H T U
       8 8 4
    – 1 5 5

    f) H T U
       4 6 6
    – 2 0 6

    g) H T U
       5 0 0
    – 2 1 2

    h) H T U
       9 0 4
    – 5 6 8

5. There were 484 petals on a rose bush, but then a strong wind blew 128 of them away. How many petals were left on the rose bush after the wind came?

6. Rewrite these downwards in your copy and solve.
    a) 144 – 97   b) 227 – 150   c) 111 – 47   d) 450 – 198

7. Clodagh saved up €6.78 last month. She gave €2.99 to her sister Ailbhe to buy a toy in Smyth's Toystore. How much money had Clodagh left?

8. Estimate the answers to these.

   a) 149 – 52   b) 194 – 107   c) 155 – 59

9. Joseph has 172 stickers. Aisling has 47 stickers less than Joseph and Niamh has 19 stickers less than Aisling.

   a) How many stickers has Niamh?

   b) How did you work out the answer? Explain.

   c) Is there any other way you could have worked out the answer? Explain.

Solve!   4. Subtraction

Calculator Mix-up

Gemma wants to type 6 + 4 into her calculator.
Gemma makes a mistake and types – instead of +.
How far from the correct answer is the number on Gemma's screen?

Strategy hints!

1. Look for the important words in the question.
2. Think logically.

Extension

Gemma wants to type 6 + 4 + 5 into her calculator.
Gemma makes a mistake and types 6 + 4 – 5.
How far from the correct answer is the number on Gemma's screen?

1. Now Is the Time to Stop

Ciarán makes a sequence of subtractions.

Copy what Ciarán did and complete the missing answers.

Explain to a friend what Ciarán did and why he stopped.

Ciarán uses the subtractions to make a chain.

215 → 164 → 118 → 37 → (stop)

Copy Ciarán's chain.

Explain to your friend how Ciarán made his chain.

> Investigate chains using start numbers from 210 to 220.

2. Is It Magical?

Rachel chooses three 2-digit numbers.   81   52   19

She uses her numbers to make 3 subtractions.

Find the answers for   and .

Make a copy of the subtractions.

Find the 3 differences between the answers for ⬠ ● and ⬡ .

Describe to a friend how you did them.

Rachel says, 'There is something magical about the 3 differences.'

What do you think is magical?

> Investigate using other three 2-digit numbers.

1. Write either **possible**, **impossible** or **certain** for each of the following sentences.

    a) I will grow to be taller than my mammy.

    b) Next week, Friday will be the day after Thursday.

    c) Next week, there will be no Tuesday.

    d) I will be able to float to school tomorrow.

    e) Ireland will win the next soccer World Cup.

    f) The sun will rise in the morning.

    g) The sun will set this evening.

    h) My pet hamster will learn to talk.

2. Number these sentences 1, 2 or 3, with 1 being the most likely to happen and 3 being the least likely.

    a) I will go to school tomorrow.

    b) I will go to the principal's office tomorrow.

    c) I will go to Australia tomorrow.

3. Number these sentences 1, 2 or 3, with 1 being the most likely to happen and 3 being the least likely.

    a) I will wear a tracksuit this week.

    b) I will wear a yellow bonnet with pink stripes this week.

    c) I will wear a uniform this week.

4. Number these sentences 1, 2 or 3, with 1 being the most likely to happen and 3 being the least likely.

    a) I will eat an apple today.

    b) I will eat chocolate today.

    c) I will eat a vegetable today.

5. Write a sentence for each picture that includes one of the following words or phrases: possible, impossible, certain, might, not sure, likely, unlikely, very likely, very unlikely. The first one has been done for you.

a) It would be impossible for these children to jump up and never come back down again.

b)

c)

d)

e)

f)

g)

h)

i)

Solve!   5. Chance

10 Boys and 10 Girls

My class has 10 boys and 10 girls in it.

The teacher, Mrs Picker, puts the names of the students into a hat.

She then takes out 3 names.

The names are all boys.

Does the next name she takes out have the best chance of being:

A boy? A girl?

Or do both boys and girls have the same chance?

Strategy hints!

1. Look for the important words in the question.
2. Think logically.

Extension

My name came out 4th. Am I most likely to be a boy or a girl?

1. Shauna's Dominoes

Shauna has a set of 28 double six dominoes.

0	0	0	0	0	0	0	1	1	1	1	1	1	2
0	1	2	3	4	5	6	1	2	3	4	5	6	2

2	2	2	2	3	3	3	3	4	4	4	5	5	6
3	4	5	6	3	4	5	6	4	5	6	5	6	6

She puts the dominoes face down, shuffles them and chooses 1 domino.

Shauna says,

"It is very likely that my domino will show a 6 because 6 is my lucky number."

Investigate the likelihood of choosing a domino with a 0, 1, 2, 3, 4, 5 or 6.

Is what Shauna said true or false?

Explain why to a friend.

2. Rolling 2 Dice

Seán rolls 2 dice and works out the total of the 2 numbers.

Seán says,

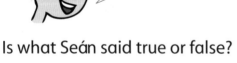

"It is impossible that the total of the two numbers is 7."

Is what Seán said true or false?

Explain to a friend how you decided.

Investigate making other likelihood statements about the total of 2 numbers on a pair of dice.

Practise!

1. Write out all of the multiplication tables for the numbers 2, 4 and 8.

2. How many legs? Work out the answer in your copy.

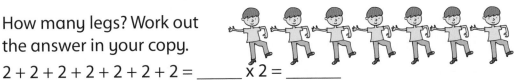

   2 + 2 + 2 + 2 + 2 + 2 + 2 = _____ x 2 = _____

3. a) ◊◊ + ◊◊ + ◊◊ + ◊◊ + ◊◊ = ___ x _____ = ___

   b) 2 + 2 = _____ x 2 = _____

4. a) 5 x 2   b) 8 x 2   c) 2 x 2   d) 6 x 2   e) 1 x 2
   f) 3 x 2   g) 7 x 2   h) 10 x 2   i) 4 x 2   j) 9 x 2

5. a) 2   b) 2   c) 2   d) 2   e) 2   f) 2   g) 2
      x 3   x 4   x 1   x 8   x 4   x 9   x 6
      ___   ___   ___   ___   ___   ___   ___

6. Can you remember your four times tables song? Try to sing it now to see if you can remember it all!

7. Write a) an addition sentence and b) a multiplication sentence in your copy for this set of pictures.

   a) ___ + ___ + ___ + ___ = _____ x _____ = _____

   b) _____ x 4 = _____

8. Write a) an addition sentence and b) a multiplication sentence for this set of pictures.

   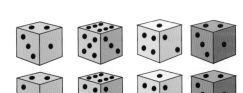

9. a) 4   b) 4   c) 4   d) 4   e) 4   f) 4   g) 4
      x 2   x 8   x 0   x 4   x 6   x 1   x 7
      ___   ___   ___   ___   ___   ___   ___

10. Continue counting in 4s. Write the answers in your copy.

    4, 8, 12, _____, _____, _____, _____, _____, _____, _____

11. 8 + 8 + 8 + 8 + 8 + 8 + 8 + 8 + 8 + 8 = ___ x ___ = ___

12. 8 + 8 + 8 + 8 = ___ x ___ = ___

13. Eight 2c pieces = _____ c

14. a)　　8　b)　　8　　　15. a)　　8　b)　　8
　　　x 7　　　x 3　　　　　　　x 5　　　x 1

16. Write a) an addition sentence and b) a multiplication sentence for this set of pictures.

17. Can you remember your eight times tables song? Try to sing it to see if you can remember it all!

18. How many seeds are in 6 packets of seeds if each packet contains 8 seeds?

19. Write 3 x 8 as an addition sentence.

20. Cathy and Anton were at Scoil Catríona's cake sale. Cathy bought 6 rice crispy buns for 8c each. She also bought 10 rock buns at 4c each and 6 fairy buns at 2c each. Anton bought 9 fairy buns, 6 rock buns and 3 rice crispy buns.

   a) How much money did Cathy spend at the cake sale?
   b) How much money did Anton spend at the cake sale?
   c) If Cathy had brought 8 times more money with her to the cake sale than she actually spent, how much money would she have brought with her?

Solve!　　　　　　　　　　　　　6. Multiplication 1

Even Steven

Steven skip counts in 2s up to 40.
How many numbers does he count?

Strategy hints!
1. Look for the important words in the question.
2. Look for a pattern.
3. Think logically.

Extension
Steven starts at 1 and skip counts in 2s up to 39.
How many numbers does he count?

1. Patterns of 4s

Ian colours the 'count on in 4s' numbers on a 7-grid.

Make a copy of what Ian did.

Explain to a friend why the grid is called a 7-grid.

Describe to your friend any patterns you notice in the 'count on in 4s' numbers in the grid.

Explain to your friend why each pattern occurs.

1	2	3	4	5	6	7
8	9	10	11	12	13	14
15	16	17	18	19	20	21
22	23	24	25	26	27	28
29	30	31	32	33	34	35
36	37	38	39	40	41	42
43	44	45	46	47	48	49

> Investigate patterns in the 'count on in 4s' numbers on a 6-grid, 8-grid and 9-grid.

2. 2 Times Table Bar Chart

Nicole makes a list of the 2 times table numbers.

Number of 2s	1	2	3	4	5	6	7	8	9	10
2 times	2	4	6							

Complete the list for Nicole.

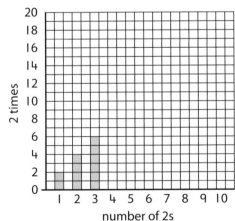

Nicole starts to draw a bar chart of the 2 times table numbers.

Copy and complete the bar chart.

Describe to a friend what you notice about the bars in the chart.

> Investigate what Nicole did for the 4 times table numbers.

1. Share these beach balls
   equally between Katie and
   Keela. Write your answers
   in your copy.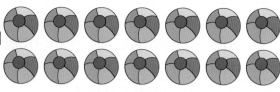

   a)   Katie and Keela get _____ beach balls each.

   b)   Now write this as a division number sentence:

   _____ ÷ _____ = _____

2. Write the division number sentences in your copy.

   a)   12 − 2 − 2 − 2 − 2 − 2 − 2 = 0, so _____ ÷ _____ = _____

   b)   2 − 2 = 0, so _____ ÷ _____ = _____

3. Bobby has 24c. With this, he can afford 3 fizzle sticks. How much is
   each fizzle stick?

4. Write out all of the division tables for the numbers 2, 4 and 8.

5. Share these
   magazines
   equally between
   Amy, Cleo, Bobby and Katie. Write your answers in your copy.

   a)   Each child gets _____ magazines.

   b)   Now write this as a division number sentence:

   _____ ÷ _____ = _____

6. Use counters or draw dots to help you get the correct answers.

   a)   4 ÷ 2   b)   8 ÷ 4   c)   14 ÷ 2   d)   28 ÷ 4   e)   4 ÷ 4

   f)   32 ÷ 4   g)   8 ÷ 2   h)   20 ÷ 2   i)   16 ÷ 4   j)   40 ÷ 4

7. Divide these sandwiches equally among Georgia and her
   7 friends. Write your answers in your copy.

   a)   Each child gets _____ sandwiches.

b) Now write this as a division number sentence:

_____ ÷ _____ = _____

8. Use counters or draw dots to help you get the correct answers.

   a) 40 ÷ 8   b) 16 ÷ 8   c) 72 ÷ 8   d) 24 ÷ 8   e) 48 ÷ 8

9. Draw circles to divide each set of pictures into groups. Then write a division number sentence and a multiplication number sentence to describe each set of pictures. Write your answers in your copy.

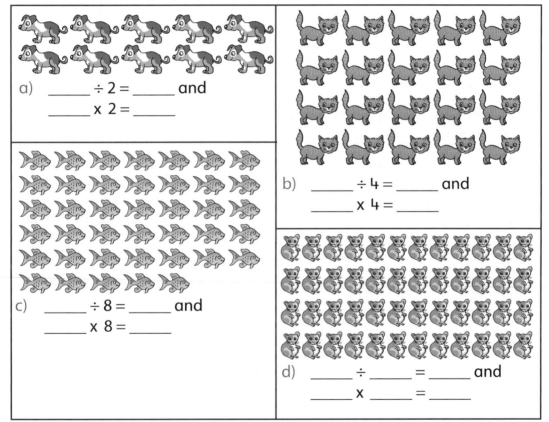

a) _____ ÷ 2 = _____ and
   _____ x 2 = _____

b) _____ ÷ 4 = _____ and
   _____ x 4 = _____

c) _____ ÷ 8 = _____ and
   _____ x 8 = _____

d) _____ ÷ _____ = _____ and
   _____ x _____ = _____

10. Sophia lined up all of her 72 dolls into 8 equal rows. How many dolls were in each row?

11. Siobhán bought a large multipack of crisps in the supermarket. There were 24 packets of crisps in the multipack, made up of 4 different flavours. How many packets of each flavour were in the multipack of crisps?

12. Use counters or draw dots if necessary to help you with these division questions. Some of them have remainders.

   a) $8 \div 2$ b) $36 \div 4$ c) $40 \div 8$ d) $18 \div 2$

   e) $19 \div 4$ f) $15 \div 2$ g) $22 \div 8$ h) $9 \div 8$

   i) $69 \div 8$ j) $30 \div 4$ k) $3 \div 2$ l) $13 \div 2$

   m) $13 \div 8$ n) $13 \div 4$ o) $55 \div 8$ p) $45 \div 4$

13. There are 80 bananas on a banana tree. If Declan the monkey eats 8 bananas from the tree every day, for how many days will Declan be able to eat bananas from the tree?

14. a) It takes Tom 2 minutes to run 1 full lap of the circular yard. If Tom runs non-stop around the yard for 17 minutes, how many full laps of the yard will he run?

   b) Will he end up at the same place he started at after 17 minutes? If not, where will he end up? Explain.

Solve! 7. Division 1

Money Share

Sanjay gives half of his money to Georgia. He has €3 left over.

How much money did Sanjay have to begin with?

Strategy hints!

1. Look for the important words in the question.
2. Work backwards.

Extension

Sanjay gives half of his money to Georgia. He then spends €1. He has €3 left over.

How much money did Sanjay have to begin with?

I. Dividing by 2, 4 and 8

Shannon draws a Venn diagram.

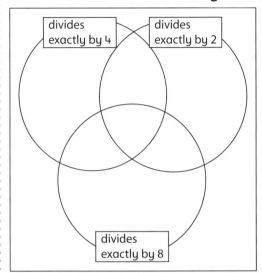

> Investigate sorting the numbers I to 40 on Shannon's Venn diagram.

2. Remainders 0, I and 2

Pádraig has 10 digit cards. | 0 | I | 2 | 3 | 4 | 5 | 6 | 7 | 8 | 9 |

He wants to use 6 of his digit cards to complete these 3 divisions correctly.

This is what he did.

| 2 | 4 | ÷ 2 = _____ R 0

| I | 7 | ÷ 4 = _____ R I

| 5 | 0 | ÷ 8 = _____ R 2

| | | ÷ 2 = _____ R 0

| | | ÷ 4 = _____ R I

| | | ÷ 8 = _____ R 2

Copy what Pádraig did.

Is what Pádraig did correct?

Explain why to a friend.

> Investigate which digits Pádraig could have used.

1. a) Draw this circle in your copy and colour $\frac{1}{2}$ of it.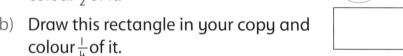

   b) Draw this rectangle in your copy and colour $\frac{1}{4}$ of it.

   c) Draw this shape in your copy and colour $\frac{1}{8}$ of it.

   d) Draw this shape in your copy and colour $\frac{1}{10}$ of it.

2. a) How many is $\frac{1}{4}$ of this set?

   b) How many is $\frac{1}{10}$ of this set?

   c) How many is $\frac{1}{8}$ of this set?

   d) How many is $\frac{1}{2}$ of these monkeys?

   e) How many is $\frac{1}{4}$ of these cupcakes?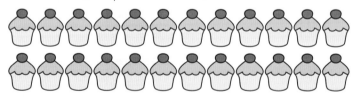

   f) How many is $\frac{1}{8}$ of these robots?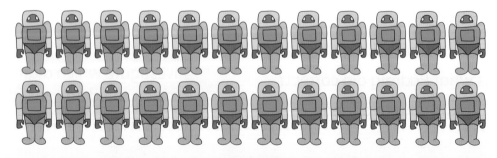

3. What fraction of the following sets is coloured?

a)   b)   c)

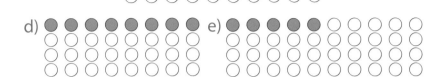

d)   e)

4. Solve the following.

a) $\frac{1}{2}$ of 14   b) $\frac{1}{4}$ of 20   c) $\frac{1}{2}$ of 20   d) $\frac{1}{4}$ of 8

e) $\frac{1}{8}$ of 48   f) $\frac{1}{10}$ of 70   g) $\frac{1}{8}$ of 72   h) $\frac{1}{10}$ of 100

5. Write these answers in your copy.

a) $\frac{1}{2} = \frac{}{4}$ b) $\frac{1}{2} = \frac{}{8}$ c) $\frac{1}{2} = \frac{}{10}$ d) $\frac{1}{4} = \frac{}{8}$

e) $\frac{2}{4} = \frac{}{2}$ f) $\frac{4}{8} = \frac{}{4}$ g) $\frac{4}{8} = \frac{}{2}$ h) $\frac{5}{10} = \frac{}{2}$

i) $1 = \frac{}{2}$ j) $1 = \frac{}{8}$

6. Write the correct symbol in your copy: greater than (>), less than (<) or equal to (=).

a) $\frac{1}{4}$ ____ $\frac{1}{8}$ b) $\frac{2}{4}$ ____ $\frac{1}{8}$ c) $\frac{2}{2}$ ____ $\frac{1}{2}$ d) $\frac{2}{4}$ ____ $\frac{1}{2}$ e) $\frac{4}{8}$ ____ $\frac{3}{4}$

f) 1 ____ $\frac{7}{8}$ g) $\frac{10}{10}$ ____ $\frac{1}{4}$ h) $\frac{1}{10}$ ____ $\frac{1}{8}$ i) 1 ____ $\frac{4}{4}$ j) $\frac{5}{10}$ ____ $\frac{2}{8}$

7. Order the following fractions from smallest to biggest.

a) $\frac{2}{4}, \frac{1}{8}, \frac{4}{10}, \frac{2}{2}$ b) $\frac{6}{8}, \frac{1}{4}, \frac{1}{2}$ c) $\frac{2}{2}, \frac{2}{4}, \frac{2}{8}$

8. Fill in the missing fractions in the patterns. Write your answers in your copy.

a) $0, \frac{1}{8},$ ____, ____, $\frac{4}{8},$ ____, ____

b) $0, \frac{1}{10}, \frac{2}{10},$ ____

c) $0,$ ____, $\frac{2}{4},$ ____, 1

9. Simon has a box of 32 Rainbow Drops. 8 of these are red. What fraction of the Rainbow Drops is red?

10. Killian's PE lesson lasts 40 minutes.
    a) If Killian does warm-ups for $\frac{1}{4}$ of the lesson, how many minutes does he spend warming up?
    b) If $\frac{1}{8}$ of the lesson is spent doing jumping jacks, how many minutes are spent doing these?
    c) 5 minutes of the lesson are spent doing forward rolls. After the warm-ups, the jumping jacks and the forward rolls, how many minutes are left for the rest of the lesson? What fraction of the lesson is this?

Solve! 9. Fractions 1

Main Town

Main Town is halfway between Ambley and Gotley.

Ambley and Gotley are 24km apart.

How far apart are Ambley and Main Town?

Strategy hints!
1. Look for the important words in the question.
2. Use a drawing.
3. Think logically.

Extension

The town of Clarke is halfway between Main Town and Gotley. Draw a map showing these 4 towns and how far apart they are.

1. Half of What?

Emily makes a rectangle on a square grid.

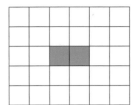

Emily says,

> My rectangle is 1 half of a whole shape. I think the whole shape looks like this.

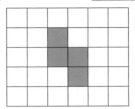

Make a copy of Emily's shape.

Is Emily correct?

Explain why to a friend.

> Investigate making other whole shapes that Emily's rectangle is 1 half of.

2. Liam's Quarters

Liam draws a square on a dotty grid.

He tries to divide his square into quarters.

This is what he did.

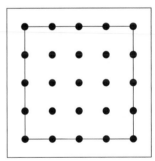

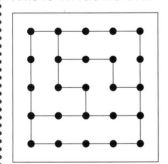

Is what Liam did correct?

Explain why to a friend.

> Investigate other ways of dividing Liam's square into quarters.

1. a) 5 x 2   b) 8 x 8   c) 6 x 2   d) 8 x 4   e) 5 x 8

    f) 7 x 4   g) 10 x 4   h) 9 x 8   i) 0 x 8   j) 1 x 4

    k) 8   l) 2   m) 4   n) 2   o) 8
        x 5   x 9   x 8   x 6   x 3

    p) 4   q) 4   r) 2   s) 8   t) 8
        x 2   x 1   x 7   x 4   x 10

2. Fill in the missing numbers in this sequence of 5s in your copy.

    5, _____, 15, _____, _____, _____, _____, _____, _____, _____, _____

3. How many fingers in total?
    Write the answer in your copy.

    5 + 5 + 5 + 5 = _____   4 x 5 = _____

4. Make multiplication sentences for the following. Write the answers in your copy.

    a) 5 + 5 + 5 + 5 + 5 = __ x __ = __

    b) 5 + 5 + 5 + 5 + 5 + 5 + 5 = __ x __ = __

    c) 5 + 5 + 5 + 5 + 5 + 5 = __ x __ = __

    d) 5 + 5 = __ x __ = __

5. Make addition sentences for the following. Write the answers in your copy.

    a) 8 x 5 = __ + __ + __ + __ + __ + __ + __ + __ = ____

    b) 3 x 5 = __ + __ + __ = ____

    c) 9 x 5 = __ + __ + __ + __ + __ + __ + __ + __ + __ = ____

6. Can you remember your five times tables song? Try to sing it now to see if you can remember it all!

7. Write out all of the multiplication tables for the numbers 5 and 10.

8. In your copy, write a) addition and b) multiplication sentences for each of the following sets of pictures.

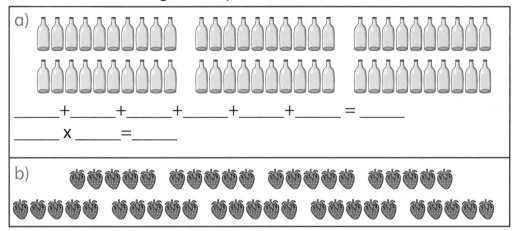

a)

_____ + _____ + _____ + _____ + _____ + _____ = _____

_____ x _____ = _____

b)

9. Draw sets of pictures in your copy to show the following.
   a) Draw puppies. 3 x 5 = _____
   b) Draw schoolbags. 2 x 10 = _____

10. In your copy, write down any number that is a multiple of 2, 4, 5, 8 or 10 from the list below.

14 5 84 63 50 4 9 80

10 7 5 25 47 14 30 64

70 3 8 24 21 17 50 13

51 37 4 12 18 16 15 54

11. Write the answers in your copy.
    a) 10 + 10 + 10 = ___ x ___ = _____
    b) 10 + 10 + 10 + 10 + 10 + 10 + 10 = ___ x ___ = _____

12. a)   5   b)   10   c)   5   d)   10   e)   10
       x 8   x 3   x 7   x 9   x 10
       ____   ____   ____   ____   ____

13. Oscar is having beans on toast for his lunch. He has 4 slices of toast with 10 beans on each slice. How many beans does Oscar have altogether?

14. Isabella is making jewellery. She puts red, yellow, pink, purple and green beads onto a piece of string. If she puts 5 beads of each colour onto the string, how many beads does she use altogether?

Solve!

Number Thinking

I am a 2-digit number.

I am less than 60.

I am in the 2s counting pattern.

I am also in the 5s counting pattern.

What is the biggest number I can be?

Strategy hints!

1. Look for the important words in the question.
2. Look for a pattern.
3. Think logically.

Extension

I am a 2-digit number.

I am between 50 and 80.

I am not in the 2s counting pattern.

I am not in the 5s counting pattern.

My 2 digits are different.

What are the biggest 3 numbers I can be?

1. John's Number Sentence

John makes up a missing numbers sentence.

$$\square + \square + \square + \square + \square = \bigcirc \times 10$$

The 5 missing numbers in the square boxes are equal.

John tries to make the number sentence true.

$$6 + 6 + 6 + 6 + 6 = 2 \times 10$$

Record what John did.

Is what John said true?

Explain to a friend how you decided.

> Investigate different ways John could make the sentence true.

2. Make Me Equal

Anna makes a missing numbers multiplication sentence.

$$6 \times \diamond = 2 \times \pentagon$$

Both and ⬠ stand for whole numbers.

This is how Anna completed her sentence.

$$6 \times 4 = 2 \times 12$$

Make a copy of what Anna did.

Is what Anna did correct?

Explain why to a friend.

> Investigate different ways Anna could complete the multiplication sentence.

1. Measure these lines and write their lengths in your copy.

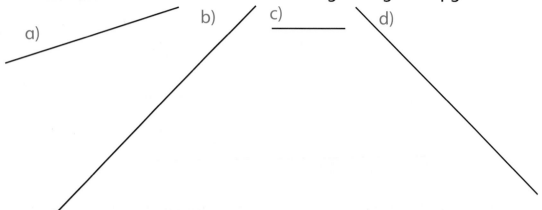

2. Find the following items and estimate their lengths. Write your estimate in your copy.

    a) pencil case   b) coin   c) copy   d) book   e) pencil

3. Now measure each item from question 2 and write their actual lengths in your copy.

    a) What is the difference between your estimate and the actual length for each item? (Subtract the smaller length from the longer length to find the difference.)

    b) Write the items in order, from shortest to longest.

    c) What would be the total length of all 5 items if they were joined together lengthways?

4. Change the following to centimetres. Write your answers in your copy.

    a) 1m 12cm = _____ cm   b) 2m 16cm = _____ cm

    c) 5m = _____ cm   d) 0m 40cm = _____ cm

    e) 5m 2cm = _____ cm   f) 3m 20cm = _____ cm

5. Change the following to metres and centimetres. Write your answers in your copy.

    a) 456cm = ___ m ___ cm   b) 815cm = ___ m ___ cm

    c) 220cm = ___ m ___ cm   d) 400cm = ___ m ___ cm

    e) 604cm = ___ m ___ cm   f) 50cm = ___ m ___ cm

6.
a)	m	cm
	4	25
+ 2		44

b)	m	cm
	2	87
– 1		56

c)	m	cm
	3	90
+ 4		09

d)	m	cm
	1	08
–		87

e)	m	cm
	5	10
– 2		85

f)	m	cm
	4	11
– 1		59

g)	m	cm
	8	71
+ 1		29

h)	m	cm
	2	00
–		85

7. Rewrite these downwards in your copy and solve.

   a) 924cm + 2m 50cm

   b) 2m 14cm – 20cm

8. Finn, Oran and Jack decided to measure the lengths of some of their toys. Finn's skateboard measured 78cm long, Oran's remote control race car measured 38cm long and Jack's pogo stick measured 1m 7cm long.

   a) What is the difference in length between Finn's skateboard and Oran's race car?

   b) How much shorter than Jack's pogo stick is Oran's race car?

   c) What is the combined length of the 3 toys?

Solve! .... 11. Length

Insect Lengths

A bee is longer than an ant.
A wasp is longer than a bee.
A flea is shorter than an ant.
List the 4 insects in order, from shortest to longest.

Strategy hints!
1. Look for the important words in the question.
2. Use a drawing.
3. Think logically.

Extension
Make up a problem like this one. List 6 animals in order, from shortest to longest.

1. Jessica's Train Set

Jessica has a train set.

The engine is 10cm long and a carriage is 8cm long.

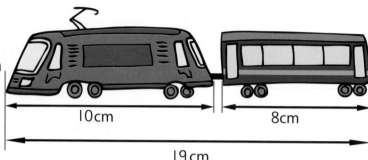

10cm

8cm

19cm

The total length of 1 engine and 1 carriage is 19cm.

What is the length of the coupling between an engine and a carriage put together?

Explain to a friend how you worked it out.

> Investigate lengths of trains with an engine and different numbers of carriages.

2. What Stephen Says

This is Stephen.

Stephen says, 'Every person is as tall as the distance from their fingertip to fingertip when their arms are stretched sideways.'

> Investigate whether what Stephan said is true of children in your class.

1. a) $15 \div 5$ b) $8 \div 8$ c) $36 \div 4$ d) $10 \div 5$ e) $12 \div 4$

    f) $48 \div 8$ g) $90 \div 10$ h) $64 \div 8$ i) $19 \div 2$ j) $45 \div 8$

    k) $26 \div 4$ l) $10 \div 8$ m) $39 \div 5$ n) $57 \div 10$ o) $16 \div 5$

2. Divide these 25 meerkats by 5. Write it as a division sentence in your copy.

3. Divide these 23 giraffes by 5. Write it as a division sentence in your copy.

4. a) $40 - 5 - 5 - 5 - 5 - 5 - 5 - 5 - 5 = 0$, so _____ $\div$ _____ = _____

    b) $30 - 5 - 5 - 5 - 5 - 5 - 5 = 0$, so _____ $\div$ _____ = _____

5. Write out all of the division tables for the numbers 5 and 10.

6. Share 18 mints equally between Siobhán, Declan, Sophia, Stephen and Brendan.

    a) How many mints does each person get?

    b) Are there any mints left over?

    c) Now write this as a division number sentence in your copy.

        _____ $\div$ _____ = _____

7. How many rows of 8 chairs can you make from 56 chairs?

8. Ann has 42 cola drops.

    a) If she shares them out equally between Shay, Thomas, Peter, Nicola and Terry, how many cola drops will each child get?

    b) How many cola drops will she have left over?

9. Rhia won €18 in a competition. She decided to keep €2 for herself and to share the rest of the winnings between 4 animal charities. How much did each charity get?

10. Copy questions a) to d) below in your copy. Divide each set of pictures into groups, then write a division and a multiplication number sentence to describe each set of pictures.

a) ___ ÷ 5 = ___ and ___ x 5 = ___	b) ___ ÷ 10 = ___ and ___ x 10 = ___
c) ___ ÷ 5 = ___ and ___ x 5 = ___	d) ___ ÷ 10 = ___ and ___ x 10 = ___

11. Draw dots or use counters, repeated subtraction, counting up or multiplying backwards to help you work out the answers to the following division questions.

a) 30 ÷ 10   b) 4⟌20   c) 8⟌16   d) $\frac{5}{5}$

e) 90 ÷ 10   f) 4⟌36   g) 5⟌10   h) $\frac{48}{8}$

i) 36 ÷ 5   j) 4⟌15   k) 5⟌17   l) $\frac{11}{2}$

m) 63 ÷ 8   n) 8⟌18   o) 8⟌19   p) $\frac{34}{5}$

q) 55 ÷ 10   r) 5⟌43   s) 4⟌26   t) $\frac{42}{5}$

Solve!   12. Division 2

20 Cents

Sasha has 20 cents in her purse.
Find 4 ways she could make
20 cents.

Strategy hints!

1. Look for the important words in the question.
2. Use a table or a chart.
3. Think logically.

Extension

a) Find all the ways Sasha can make 25 cents.
b) Find all the ways Sasha can make 50 cents.

1. James's Division by 10

James makes divisions by 10 of numbers from 10 to 19.

Complete the missing divisions.

Explain to a friend how you did them.

Put the divisions in order.

Describe patterns in the divisions to a friend.

10	÷	10	=	1	remainder	0
14	÷	10	=	1	remainder	
18	÷	10	=		remainder	
11	÷	10	=		remainder	
15	÷		=		remainder	
19	÷		=		remainder	
12	÷		=		remainder	
17	÷		=		remainder	
16	÷		=		remainder	
13	÷		=		remainder	

Investigate making divisions by 10 of the numbers 20, 21, 22, 23 … 29.

2. Patrick's Sorting Grid

Patrick draws this sorting grid.

	When divided by 2 the remainder is 0.	When divided by 2 the remainder is 1.
When divided by 3 the remainder is 0.		
When divided by 5 the remainder is 0.		
When divided by 8 the remainder is 0.		
When divided by 10 the remainder is 0.		

Investigate sorting the numbers 1 to 40 in the grid.

1. Draw these in your copy and continue each pattern. (It may help you to 'read' each pattern aloud.)

    a)

    b)

    c)

    d)

    e)

2. Continue the following in your copy and explain the rule.

3. Continue the following in your copy and explain the rule.

4. Write the next 5 numbers in this sequence in your copy.

    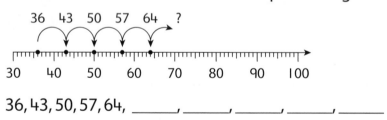

    36, 43, 50, 57, 64, _____, _____, _____, _____, _____

5. Continue these number sequences in your copy and explain the rule each time.

    a) 3, 6, 9, 12, 15, 18, _____, _____, _____

    b) 11, 13, 15, 17, 19, _____, _____, _____

    c) 45, 55, 65, 75, 85, _____, _____, _____

d) 1, 12, 23, 34, 45, _____, _____, _____

e) 4, 8, 16, 32, 64, _____, _____, _____

f) 987, 887, 787, 687, 587, _____, _____, _____

g) 450, 445, 440, 435, 430, _____, _____, _____

h) 105, 106, 108, 111, 115, _____, _____, _____

Solve!   13. Number Patterns and Sequences

Birthday Bonanza

Abbey is given €1 on her 1st birthday, €2 on her 2nd birthday, €4 on her 3rd birthday and €8 on her 4th birthday.

a) What is happening to her presents?

b) How much did Abbey get on her 5th birthday?

Strategy hints!

1. Look for the important words in the question.
2. Look for a pattern.
3. Think logically.

Extension

a) How old is Abbey when she is given €32?

b) How old is Abbey when she is given €128?

1. 2-Storey Houses

Grace makes a sequence of 2-storey houses.

    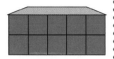

house 1   house 2   house 3   house 4   house 5

Make Grace's sequence of 2-storey houses.

How many squares did you need for each house?

Describe to a friend how you decided.

Predict how many squares you will need to make the next house in the sequence.

Extend Grace's sequence.

Investigate Grace's sequence of houses.

2. Counters and Sticks

     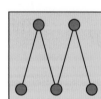   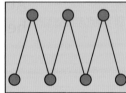

number of counters ☐   number of counters ☐   number of counters ☐

number of sticks ☐   number of sticks ☐   number of sticks ☐

Connor starts to make a sequence pattern with counters and sticks.

Make Connor's pattern.

Complete the missing numbers of counters and sticks.

Explain what you did to a friend.

Predict how many counters and sticks you will need to make pattern 4.

Investigate Connor's sequence.

1. In your copy, write out all of the sets of multiplication tables for every number from 2 up to 10.

2. $9 + 9 + 9 =$ ___ x ___ = ___

3. $6 + 6 + 6 + 6 + 6 =$ ___ x ___ = ___

4. 8 x 3cm = ___cm

5. Seven 10c pieces = ____c

6. Continue counting in 6s: 6, 12, ___, ___, ___, ___, ___, ___, ___

7. How many sweets are in 9 packets of sweets if each packet contains 6 sweets?

8. Write 5 x 5 as an addition sentence.

9. Ask the person next to you to pick any number between 3 and 9. Sing the Karaoke Times Tables Song.

10. How many multiplication sentences can you think of that make 30? Write your answers in your copy.

11. How many multiplication sentences can you think of that make 12? Write your answers in your copy.

12. There are 7 trays of eggs stacked on a supermarket shelf. Each tray contains 8 rows of 6 eggs. How many eggs are on the supermarket shelf?

13. Ms Devlin divided her class into 4 groups: Leinster, Ulster, Munster and Connaught. There were 9 children in the Leinster group and she gave them each 10 lollipop sticks. There were 6 children in the Ulster group and she gave them each 5 lollipop sticks. There were 5 children in the Munster group and she gave them each 8 lollipop sticks. There were 7 children in the Connaught group and she gave them each 4 lollipop sticks. If there were 190 lollipop

sticks in the packet before Ms Devlin started handing them out,
how many lollipop sticks were left in the packet afterwards?

Solve! · 15. Multiplication 3

Column Craft

Numbers have been put into certain columns in a table.

A	B	C
35	14	20
75	90	50
90	78	80
25	30	60
40	98	90

What type of number is in column A?

What type of number is in column B?

What type of number is in column C?

Strategy hints!

1. Look for the important words in the question.
2. Look for a pattern.
3. Use a table or a chart.

Extension

a) Why is the number 90 in all 3 columns?

b) How many numbers less than 100 could be in all 3 columns?

1. Close to 100

Tara has 9 digit cards.

1	2	3	4	5	6	7	8	9

She wants to use 3 of her digit cards to complete this calculation so that the answer is as close as possible to 100.

$$(\boxed{} \times 3) + (\boxed{} \times 6) + (\boxed{} \times 9)$$

This is what Tara did.

$$(\boxed{5} \times 3) + (\boxed{2} \times 6) + (\boxed{7} \times 9)$$

Make a copy of what Tara did.

Work out the answer to Tara's calculation.

How close to 100 is the answer to her calculation?

Explain how you worked it out to a friend.

> Investigate using different sets of 3 digits for Tara's calculation.

2. Pattern in Digital Roots

Mark writes the multiplication table for 7.

For each product, he finds the digital root.

Explain to a friend how Mark finds the digital root of a number.

Complete and extend the 7 times table and the digital roots.

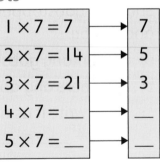

$1 \times 7 = 7$	7
$2 \times 7 = 14$	5
$3 \times 7 = 21$	3
$4 \times 7 = \underline{}$	___
$5 \times 7 = \underline{}$	___

Mark begins to draw a diagram to show the pattern in the digital roots.

Complete the diagram.

Explain the pattern to a friend.

> Investigate digital root patterns for the 3, 6 and 9 times tables.

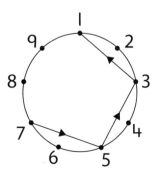

1. a) $24 \div 4$ b) $5\,|\,\overline{20}$ c) $8\,|\,\overline{64}$ d) $\frac{90}{10}$

   e) $23 \div 4$ f) $2\,|\,\overline{11}$ g) $5\,|\,\overline{48}$ h) $\frac{70}{8}$

2. Share a packet of 30 stickers equally between Lucy, Grace and Bella.
   a) How many stickers does each girl get?
   b) Are there any stickers left over?
   c) Now write it as a division number sentence in your copy.
      _____ ÷ _____ = _____

3. There are 18 spoons in 6 rows on a tray. How many spoons are in each row?

4. a) How many tubes of 9 sweets can be made from 85 sweets?
   b) How many sweets are left over?

5. a) $21 \div 3$ b) $6\,|\,\overline{48}$ c) $7\,|\,\overline{56}$ d) $\frac{63}{9}$

   e) $66 \div 7$ f) $9\,|\,\overline{20}$ g) $3\,|\,\overline{28}$ h) $\frac{50}{6}$

6. Share 42 gobstoppers equally between Katie, Keela, Cleo, Amy and Bobby.
   a) How many gobstopper does each child get?
   b) Are there any gobstoppers left over?
   c) Now write it as a division number sentence in your copy.
      _____ ÷ _____ = _____

7. a) How many full sets of 3 are in 24?
   b) Is there a remainder? ($24 \div 3 =$ ___R___)

8. a) How many full sets of 7 are in 65?
   b) Is there a remainder? ($65 \div 7 =$ _____R___)

9. Write your answers in your copy.
   a) $40 - 5 - 5 - 5 - 5 - 5 - 5 - 5 - 5 = 0$, so _____ ÷ _____ = _____
   b) $45 - 9 - 9 - 9 - 9 - 9 = 0$, so _____ ÷ _____ = _____

10. Write 4 correct multiplication and division number sentences, using the 3 numbers in each set.

For example, 3, 8, 24: $3 \times 8 = 24$ $8 \times 3 = 24$ $24 \div 3 = 8$ $24 \div 8 = 3$

a) 2, 9, 18   b) 4, 8, 32   c) 6, 30, 5   d) 72, 8, 9

11. Write out all of the division tables for the numbers 3, 6, 9 and 7.

12. Draw dots or use counters, repeated subtraction, counting up or multiplying backwards to help you work out the answers to the following division questions.

a) $21 \div 3$ b) $6\overline{)24}$ c) $9\overline{)81}$ d) $\frac{28}{7}$

e) $32 \div 6$ f) $3\overline{)20}$ g) $4\overline{)25}$ h) $\frac{15}{9}$

i) $23 \div 5$ j) $7\overline{)13}$ k) $8\overline{)54}$ l) $\frac{21}{10}$

m) $65 \div 10$ n) $2\overline{)23}$ o) $6\overline{)14}$ p) $\frac{10}{1}$

Solve!   16. Division 3

2 Books High

2 books are on a table on top of each other.

1 book is twice as thick as the other book.

Together, the books are 6cm thick.

How thick are the 2 books?

Strategy hints!

1. Look for the important words in the question.
2. Have a go.
3. Think logically.

Extension

2 books are on a table on top of each other.
1 book is twice as thick as the other book.
Together, the books are 15cm thick.
How thick are the 2 books?

1. Circle Numbers

Tomás has 3 subtractions with missing 2-digit numbers and a 5 in each circle.

☐☐ – ⑤ – ⑤ = 0
☐☐ – ⑤ – ⑤ – ⑤ = 0
☐☐ – ⑤ – ⑤ – ⑤ – ⑤ = 0

Tomás completed the subtractions.

Is what Tomás did correct?

Explain why to a friend.

| 1 | 0 | – ⑤ – ⑤ = 0
| 1 | 5 | – ⑤ – ⑤ – ⑤ = 0
| 2 | 0 | – ⑤ – ⑤ – ⑤ – ⑤ = 0

Investigate 2-digit numbers when a different number is in the circles.

2. Elizabeth's Buttons

Elizabeth has a jar of buttons.

She says, 'When I arrange them in 2s there is 1 button left over.

When I arrange them in 3s there are 2 buttons left over.

When I arrange them in 5s there are 4 buttons left over.'

Jordan says, 'There are 29 buttons in the jar.'

Could what Jordan said be true?

Explain why to a friend.

Investigate other possible numbers of buttons that could be in the jar.

1. Draw this shape in your copy, then colour $\frac{1}{4}$ of it red.

2. What fraction of this shape is shaded?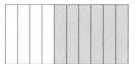

3. Draw this shape in your copy, then colour $\frac{3}{8}$ of it blue.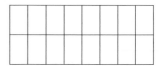

4. Draw this set into your copy, then colour $\frac{1}{2}$ of it green.

5. What fraction of each of the following sets is shaded?

   a)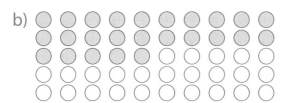

   b)

   c)   d)

   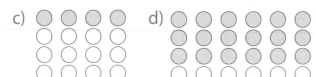

6. Answer these in your copy.

   a) $\frac{1}{4}$ of 4   b) $\frac{1}{8}$ of 24   c) $\frac{1}{2}$ of 2   d) $\frac{1}{10}$ of 10

   e) $\frac{1}{2}$ of 46   f) $\frac{1}{10}$ of 60   g) $\frac{1}{8}$ of 56   h) $\frac{1}{10}$ of 100

   i) $\frac{1}{4}$ of 52   j) $\frac{1}{4}$ of 72   k) $\frac{1}{2}$ of 2   l) $\frac{1}{8}$ of 32

   m) $\frac{1}{4}$ of 64   n) $\frac{1}{8}$ of 16   o) $\frac{1}{2}$ of 100   p) $\frac{1}{4}$ of 60

7. Find the whole number. Write your answer in your copy.

   a) $\frac{1}{2}$ = 9, so the whole number = _____

   b) $\frac{1}{4}$ = 5, so the whole number = _____

   c) $\frac{1}{8}$ = 7, so the whole number = _____

   d) $\frac{1}{10}$ = 3, so the whole number = _____

8. Write your answers in your copy.

   a) $\frac{1}{2}$ of ___ = 5   b) $\frac{1}{4}$ of ___ = 6   c) $\frac{1}{8}$ of ___ = 2

   d) $\frac{1}{10}$ of ___ = 5   e) $\frac{1}{2}$ of ___ = 8   f) $\frac{1}{4}$ of ___ = 13

   g) $\frac{1}{8}$ of ___ = 4   h) $\frac{1}{10}$ of ___ = 9   i) $\frac{1}{8}$ of ___ = 1

   j) $\frac{1}{2}$ of ___ = 57   k) $\frac{1}{10}$ of ___ = 7   l) $\frac{1}{4}$ of ___ = 24

   m) $\frac{1}{10}$ of ___ = 10c   n) $\frac{1}{4}$ of ___ = 250m

   o) $\frac{1}{8}$ of ___ = 6 mins   p) $\frac{1}{2}$ of ___ = 500g

9. Niall baked a giant cupcake and covered it with sprinkles. He covered $\frac{1}{2}$ of it with blue sprinkles, $\frac{1}{4}$ of it with red sprinkles, $\frac{1}{8}$ of it with silver sprinkles and the rest of it with chocolate sprinkles. What fraction of the cake did Niall cover with chocolate sprinkles?

10. Bella spent $\frac{3}{4}$ of €8.60. How much money did she have left?

Solve!   17. Fractions 2

Pencils and Rulers

How many rulers will be the same length as 12 pencils?

Strategy hints!
1. Look for the important words in the question.
2. Use a drawing.
3. Think logically.

Extension

4 pencils are the same length as 1 ruler.

How many pencils are the same length as 9 rulers?

1. Colouring Fractions

Aaron draws a 2 x 4 rectangle.

He colours his rectangle $\frac{1}{2}$ red and $\frac{1}{4}$ green.

Make a copy of what Aaron did.

Is what Aaron did correct?

Explain why to a friend.

What fraction of the rectangle is not coloured?

Explain to your friend how you worked it out.

Complete these calculations.

$\frac{1}{2}$ of 8 = ☐ $\frac{1}{4}$ of 8 = ☐ $\frac{2}{8}$ of 8 = ☐

Explain to your friend how you did them.

Investigate colouring different rectangles $\frac{1}{2}$ red and $\frac{1}{4}$ green.

2. 4 Digits Are Missing

Caoimhe has 9 digit cards. | 0 | 2 | 3 | 4 | 5 | 6 | 7 | 8 | 9 |

There is no 1 digit, as Caoimhe has already used it in this statement.

Caoimhe wants to complete this fraction statement using 4 of her cards.

This is what she did.

Make a copy of what Caoimhe did.

Is what she did correct?

Explain why to a friend.

$\frac{1}{☐}$ of ☐☐ = ☐

$\frac{1}{3}$ of 2 7 = 9

Investigate using 4 digit cards to complete the statement in different ways.

1. a) Draw this shape in your copy and colour 0.1 of it red.

   b) Write 0.1 as a fraction.

2. a) Draw this shape in your copy and colour 0.9 of it blue.

   b) Write 0.9 as a fraction.

3. a) Draw this shape in your copy and colour 0.3 of it.

   b) Write 0.3 as a fraction.

4. a) Draw this shape in your copy and colour 0.5 of it.

   b) Write 0.5 as a fraction.

5. What portion of this shape is shaded?

   a) Write it as a fraction.

   b) Write it as a decimal.

6. What portion of this shape is shaded?

   a) Write it as a fraction.

   b) Write it as a decimal.

7. a) How much is shaded yellow? Write it as a decimal.

   b) How much is shaded white? Write it as a decimal.

8. Draw this shape in your copy and colour in these decimal values.

   a) Red = 0.2　　　　b) Blue = 0.1　　　　c) Yellow = 0.7

9. Draw this shape in your copy and colour 1.7.

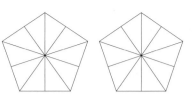

10. Draw this shape in your copy and colour 2.8.

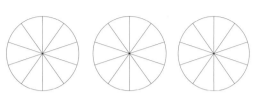

11. Draw this shape in your copy and colour 1.6.

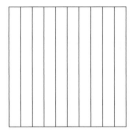 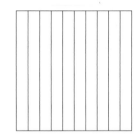

12. Draw this shape in your copy and colour 3.2.

13. Which number has the greatest value: 0.2, 0.7 or 0.4?
Fill in the above values on this number line to see if you were correct.

```
0          0.5          1.0
```

14. Which number has the smallest value: 0.3, 0.8 or 0.1?
Fill in the above values on this number line to see if you were correct.

```
0          0.5          1.0
```

15. Which number has the greatest value: 0.6, 1.6, 1.2 or 0.4?
Fill in the above values on this number line to see if you were correct.

```
0      0.5      1.0      1.5      2.0
```

16. Every row, column and diagonal in this magic square adds up to the number 4.5. Can you fill in all of the empty spaces in the magic square correctly?

Decimal Magic Square

	0.9	
0.6		1.8

Solve! 18. Decimals

Toy Sale

Sami bought some toys at a sale.

These toys were for sale.

Sami spent €0.90 and bought 4 toys.

What did Sami buy?

€0.30

€0.10

€0.20

Extension

See if you can find more than 1 answer that works.

Strategy hints!

1. Look for the important words in the question.
2. Use a drawing.
3. Think logically.

Investigate!

1. Is Ryan's Total 1?

Ryan has 9 decimal number cards.

| 0.1 | 0.2 | 0.3 | 0.4 | 0.5 | 0.6 | 0.7 | 0.8 | 0.9 |

He puts 3 of his cards at the corners of a triangle so that the total is 1.

Make a copy of Ryan's triangle.

Is the total of Ryan's numbers equal to 1?

Explain to a friend how you decided.

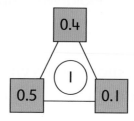

Investigate ways of completing the triangle correctly.

2. Decimal Jumping

Caitríona has a 0 to 1 decimal number line marked in tenths.

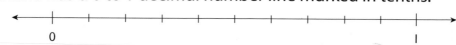

She draws a jump of 2 tenths on her number line.

Caitríona says, 'I started at 0.3 and ended on 0.5.'

Make a copy of what Caitríona did.

Is what Caitríona said correct?

Explain why to a friend.

Investigate making jumps of 2 tenths, 3 tenths and 4 tenths on a 0 to 1 decimal number line.

You will need a number of packs of cards
(supplied with this maths series).

1. How many cards will it take to cover the area of the cover of your
   maths book? Write your answers in your copy.

   Estimate = _____cards   Actual area = _____ cards

2. How many cards will it take to cover the area of the cover of your
   maths copy? Write your answers in your copy.

   Estimate = _____cards   Actual area = _____ cards

3. How many cards will it take to cover the area of the top of your
   seat?

   Estimate = _____cards   Actual area = _____ cards

4. Look at the shapes below. Which of the shapes do you think
   covers the largest area of the grid?

5. Which of the shapes do you think has the smallest area?

6. Measure the area of each of these shapes and write the
   measurements in square units.

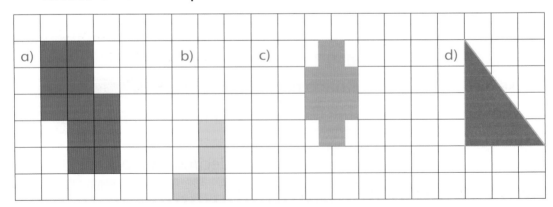

7. a) Thinking of the squares in your maths copy, estimate the area that your pencil case will cover in square units.

    b) Now place the pencil case onto the squares in your maths copy and draw around it.

    c) Count up the number of squares that were covered to find the area covered.

8. In your maths copy, draw and label a square measuring 25 square units. Always use a ruler!

9. In your maths copy, draw and label a rectangle with an area of 16 square units.

10. In your maths copy, draw and label a hexagon measuring 5 square units.

Solve!   20. Area

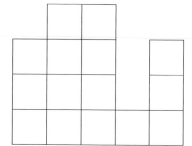

Missing Parts

This shape has some blocks missing.
How many blocks need to be added to finish it off?

Strategy hints!

1. Look for the important words in the question.
2. Use a drawing.
3. Think logically.

Extension

How many more blocks need to be added to the shape to make it a square?

1. Stick Shapes

Rebecca has 12 sticks.

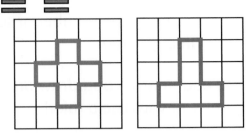

She uses the sticks to make 2 shapes on square grids.

Make a copy of what Rebecca did.

Check that she used 12 sticks each time.

Describe to a friend how you decided.

What is the area of each of Rebecca's shapes?

Explain how you worked them out to your friend.

> Investigate areas of shapes made using 12 sticks.

2. Shoes

Laura draws around her right shoe on squared paper.

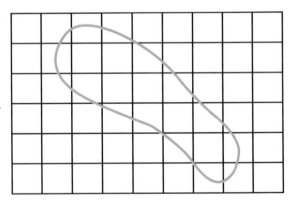

Work out the total number of squares Laura's drawing of her shoe covers.

What is the area of the drawing of the shoe?

Explain to a friend how you worked it out.

Laura says, 'Boys' shoes have a greater area than girls' shoes.'

> Investigate what Laura said.

1. Write the following as euro. Use the € symbol.

    a) 543c   b) 131c   c) 657c   d) 835c

    e) 136c   f) 478c   g) 235c   h) 142c

    i) 219c   j) 750c   k) 307c   l) 470c

    m) 24c   n) 11c   o) 27c   p) 99c

    q) 36c   r) 50c   s) 92c   t) 3c

2. Write the following in cents. Use the c symbol.

    a) €5.25   b) €1.47   c) €2.46   d) €3.89

    e) €1.65   f) €1.77   g) €8.98   h) €9.99

    i) €7.91   j) €3.60   k) €2.80   l) €9.00

    m) €0.42   n) €0.91   o) €0.12   p) €0.14

    q) €0.72   r) €0.20   s) €4.05   t) €0.02

3. Add the following amounts of money.

    a)   €2.24   b)   €2.94   c)   €4.77   d)   €8.43   e)   €2.14
       + €1.19   + €6.34   + €3.99   + €3.67   + €11.80

4. Subtract the following amounts of money.

    a)   €5.55   b)   €9.61   c)   €6.87   d)   €8.40   e)   €7.42
       − €2.21   − €7.40   − €2.99   − €5.51   − €1.03

5. Killian is counting up the money in his piggy bank. He has €2.19
    in total, made up of 11 coins. These are some of the coins: 1c, 2c, 5c,
    10c, 20c and €1.
    What might the rest of the coins be?

40 Cents

Isla has 40 cents in her purse.

Isla has only 7 coins.

Which coins are in Isla's purse?

Strategy hints!

1. Look for the important words in the question.
2. Think logically.

Extension

Using only 10 cent and 20 cent coins, find all the ways you can make 40 cents.

1. Leah Buys a Drink

Leah buys a drink for 20c.

She uses 1c, 2c and 10c coins to pay for the drink.

Leah says, 'I paid for the drink with one 10c,
four 2c and two 1c coins.'

Did Leah pay the correct amount?

Explain to a friend how you
decided.

> Investigate which coins
> Leah could have used to
> pay for the drink.

2. Paper Money

Jamie goes shopping.
He buys these 4 items.

€1.30   80c   20c   €2.50 per pack

Jamie says, 'If I pay using a €5 note, I would get 20c change.'

Is what Jamie said correct?

Explain how you decided to a
friend.

> Investigate the change Jamie
> should be given if he paid using
> a different value note.

1. Look around your classroom to find 6 objects that have line symmetry.

   Sketch each of these objects in your copy and label the pictures.

2. Trace these shapes into your copy. Colour the symmetrical shapes green and draw their line (or lines) of symmetry onto the shape. Colour the non-symmetrical shapes red.

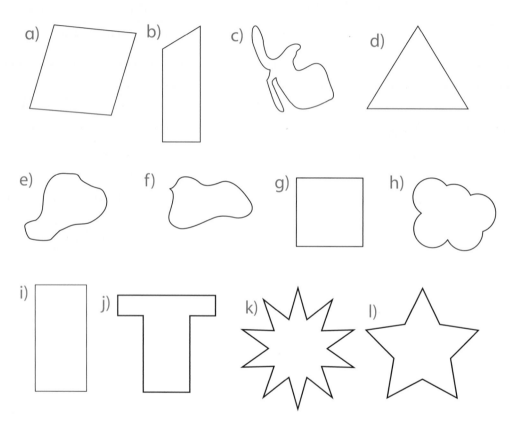

3. Draw 3 symmetrical shapes, patterns or pictures in your copy and draw their lines of symmetry.

Cut It Out

Jacob folds a piece of paper in half and cuts out a piece.
He then unfolds it.
What will it look like?

Extension

Sally folds a piece of paper in half and cuts out a piece.
She then unfolds it.
What will it look like?

Strategy hints!

1. Look for the important words in the question.
2. Use a drawing.
3. Make a model.

1. Symmetrical Patterns

Saoirse has a 5 x 5 square grid.

She colours 5 squares.

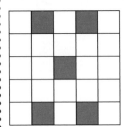

Make a copy of what Saoirse did.

Saoirse says, 'I have made a symmetrical pattern.'

Is what Saoirse said true?

Explain why to a friend.

How many mirror lines does Saoirse's pattern have?

Explain to your friend how you decided.

> Investigate colouring 3, 4, 5 and 6 squares to make symmetrical patterns on a 5 x 5 square grid.

2. Using Triangles

Mark has lots of identical triangles with equal sides.

He uses 3 of his triangles to make a shape that has 1 line of symmetry.

Make a copy of what Mark did.

Does Mark's shape have 1 line of symmetry?

Draw the line of symmetry.

How many sides does Mark's shape have?

Explain to a friend how you worked it out.

> Investigate using 2, 3, 4, etc. triangles to make shapes that have only 1 line of symmetry.

1. Write your answers in your copy.

    a) $5 \times 9 = 9 \times 5 = \underline{\hphantom{00}}$

    b) $3 \times 8 = \underline{\hphantom{00}} \times \underline{\hphantom{00}} = \underline{\hphantom{00}}$

    c) $4 \times 2 = \underline{\hphantom{00}} \times \underline{\hphantom{00}} = \underline{\hphantom{00}}$

    d) $7 \times \underline{\hphantom{00}} = \underline{\hphantom{00}} \times \underline{\hphantom{00}} = 42$

    e) $\underline{\hphantom{00}} \times 7 = \underline{\hphantom{00}} \times 4 = \underline{\hphantom{00}}$

    f) $2 \times \underline{\hphantom{00}} = 10 \times \underline{\hphantom{00}} = \underline{\hphantom{00}}$

    g) $8 \times 0 = \underline{\hphantom{00}} \times \underline{\hphantom{00}} = \underline{\hphantom{00}}$

    h) $\underline{\hphantom{00}} \times 3 = 3 \times \underline{\hphantom{00}} = 27$

    i) $\underline{\hphantom{00}} \times \underline{\hphantom{00}} = \underline{\hphantom{00}} \times \underline{\hphantom{00}} = 24$

2. Write 2 multiplication sentences and their answers for each of these number puzzles. The first one has been started for you.

    a)
18	
2	9

    $2 \times 9 = \underline{\hphantom{00}}$
    $\underline{\hphantom{00}} \times 2 = 18$

    b)
56	
7	?

    c)
28	
?	?

3. Solve these number sentences. Write your answers in your copy.

    a) $8 \times 4 = (6 \times 4) + (2 \times 4) = \underline{\hphantom{00}}$ $8 \times 4 = 24 + 8 = 32$

    b) $6 \times 7 = (5 \times 7) + (1 \times 7) = \underline{\hphantom{00}}$ $6 \times 7 = \underline{\hphantom{00}} + \underline{\hphantom{00}} = \underline{\hphantom{00}}$

    c) $12 \times 4 = (10 \times 4) + (? \times 4) = \underline{\hphantom{00}}$ $12 \times 4 = \underline{\hphantom{00}} + \underline{\hphantom{00}} = \underline{\hphantom{00}}$

    d) $11 \times 8 = (\underline{\hphantom{00}} \times 8) + (\underline{\hphantom{00}} \times 8) = \underline{\hphantom{00}}$ $11 \times 8 = \underline{\hphantom{00}} + \underline{\hphantom{00}} = \underline{\hphantom{00}}$

4. a)   15   b)   21   c)   48   d)   33   e)   50
        $\times\ 3$ $\times\ 9$ $\times\ 6$ $\times\ 9$ $\times\ 8$

5. Estimate the answers to the questions below and then work out the answers properly in your copy.

    a) 31×3 b) 69×2 c) 58×4 d) 19×7

6. If there are 4 classes in St Vincent's Senior School with 29 children in each class, how many children are in the school altogether? Estimate first and then work out the answer properly.

7. There are 11 rows of 42 children at an assembly. How many children are at the assembly altogether? Estimate first and then work out the answer properly.

8. Solve the puzzle. Who is this inspirational leader?

22 x 5	25 x 8	46 x 7		99 x 3	44 x 6	18 x 9	8 x 33	15 x 4		81 x 2	4 x 66	71 x 5	88 x 3

110 = T   297 = D   355 = M   60 = I
200 = H   162 = L   322 = E   264 = A

Solve! .... 23. Multiplication 4

Column Craft

12	18	27
36	42	45
10	6	18
18	54	63
60	24	90

What type of number is in column A?

What type of number is in column B?

What type of number is in column C?

> **Extension**
> a) Why is number 18 in all 3 columns?
> b) What other numbers under 100 could go in all 3 columns?

1. A Multiplication Wall

Adrian makes this multiplication wall, which starts with the numbers 2, 1, 3 and 4 in row 1.

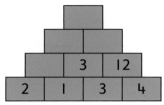

The number in each box is found by multiplying the 2 numbers below it.

Complete the multiplication wall for Adrian.

Explain to a friend how you did this.

> Investigate multiplication walls with 1, 2, 3 and 4 in different orders.

2. More Than and More Than

Cian has 10 digit cards and a missing digits 'more than' statement .

| 0 | 1 | 2 | 3 | 4 | 5 | 6 | 7 | 8 | 9 |

| 4 | | × 1 > | 2 | | × 2 > | 1 | | × 3 |

He chooses 3 of his digit cards to make his 'more than' statement true.

This is what Cian did.

| 4 | 7 | × 1 > | 2 | 3 | × 2 > | 1 | 2 | × 3 |

47   46   36

TRUE or FALSE

Make a copy of what Cian did.

Is what Cian did true or false?

Explain why to a friend.

> Investigate ways of completing Cian's statement.

1. Write the names of the shapes in your copy.

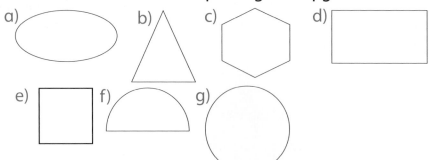

2. Which of the following are irregular shapes?

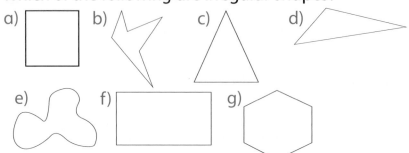

3. Which of the following shapes are hexagons?

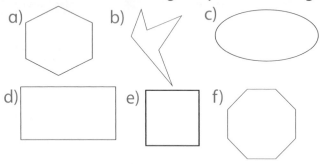

4. Which of the following shapes will tessellate?

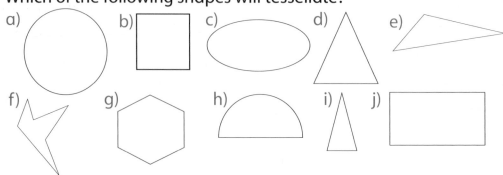

5. Find objects in your classroom that show the following 2-D shapes. Copy this table and fill it in.

2-D Shape	Draw 2-D Shape	Name of Object	Draw Picture of Object
a) Oval			
b) Triangle			
c) Rectangle			
d) Square			
e) Semi-circle			
f) Hexagon			
g) Circle			

Solve!

Something Different

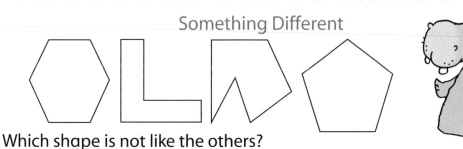

Which shape is not like the others?

Extension

Make up a problem like this one.

See if a classmate can work it out.

Strategy hints!

1. Look for the important words in the question.
2. Use a drawing.
3. Think logically.

1. Caitlin's Triangles

Caitlin has lots of 3x3 dotty grids.

She draws 3 different triangles on her grids.

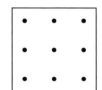

 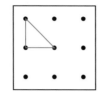

Copy Caitlin's triangles.

Explain to a friend how you did this.

How many sides does each triangle have?

How many corners does each triangle have?

Explain to your friend how you did these.

Describe to your friend ways in which the triangles are different.

Investigate drawing different triangles on 3x3 dotty grids.

2. A Ring of Hexagons

Róisín has lots of identical regular hexagons.

She uses some of her hexagons to make a ring.

Copy and colour Róisín's ring.

How many hexagons did Róisín use to make her ring?

Explain to a friend how you worked it out.

Make Róisín's ring with your own hexagons.

Explain to your friend how you did this.

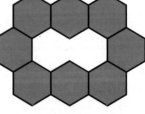

Investigate making your own hexagon rings.

1. a) $10 \div 2$ b) $4\overline{)4}$ c) $8\overline{)64}$ d) $\frac{25}{5}$

   e) $15 \div 3$ f) $7\overline{)21}$ g) $9\overline{)45}$ h) $\frac{30}{6}$

   i) $11 \div 10$ j) $4\overline{)29}$ k) $3\overline{)14}$ l) $\frac{58}{8}$

   m) $33 \div 5$ n) $7\overline{)44}$ o) $6\overline{)40}$ p) $\frac{40}{9}$

2. Share a packet of 49 peanuts equally between Katie, Dara, Lily, Maedbh and Conor.

   a) How many peanuts does each child get?

   b) Are there any peanuts left over?

   c) Now write it as a division number sentence in your copy.

     _____ ÷ _____ = _____

3. a) $6\overline{)75}$ b) $8\overline{)96}$ c) $3\overline{)81}$ d) $6\overline{)66}$ e) $2\overline{)84}$

   f) $4\overline{)76}$ g) $5\overline{)95}$ h) $7\overline{)84}$ i) $8\overline{)80}$ j) $9\overline{)90}$

4. Alma has a piece of ribbon that is 64cm long. If she cuts the piece of ribbon into quarters, how long will each new piece of ribbon be?

5. a) $5\overline{)64}$ b) $9\overline{)92}$ c) $4\overline{)21}$ d) $6\overline{)64}$ e) $3\overline{)59}$

   f) $2\overline{)97}$ g) $7\overline{)50}$ h) $6\overline{)88}$ i) $8\overline{)14}$ j) $7\overline{)12}$

6. Rewrite these questions in your copy in one of the styles used in question 1 above before working out the answers.

   a) $24 \div 5$ b) $81 \div 7$ c) $46 \div 4$ d) $22 \div 8$

   e) $\frac{58}{6}$ f) $\frac{44}{9}$ g) $\frac{62}{3}$

7. Answer the questions using the information and the diagram below.

Doll's House Bedroom Floor Plan

Information:

The bedroom floor of the doll's house is a square shape.

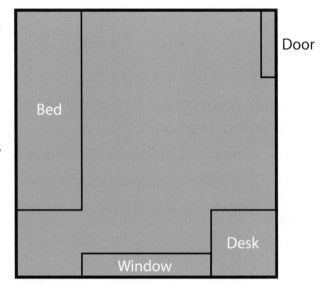

The window is half the length of 1 wall.

The surface of the desk is square.

The width of the bed is 9cm.

The width of the bed is one-third of its length.

The desk takes up one-quarter of the length of the wall with the window.

The width of the door is the same as the length of the desk.

The wall that the bed is against is 36cm long.

The width of the bed is the same as the length of each side of the desk.

a) What length is the wall that the bed is against?

b) What length is the window?

c) What length is the surface of the desk?

d) What width is the surface of the desk?

e) What length is the bed?

f) How wide is the door?

g) How much free space is there continuing along the wall at the end of the bed?

h) If you were to fit a wardrobe in the empty space against the wall beside the window, what is the maximum width that the wardrobe could be?

50 Cents

Ciara has 4 coins. She only has 2 different types of coins.

She has 50 cents altogether.

What 4 coins does Ciara have?

Extension

What is the biggest amount of money Ciara can have with 4 coins?

Strategy hints!

1. Look for the important words in the question.
2. Think logically.

1. Packets of Crayons

Mr Flynn makes 8 packets of crayons.

He says, 'I can share the crayons equally between Dean and Kelly and not open the packets.'

Mrs O'Neill thinks that Dean should get packets with 1, 3, 6 and 8 crayons and Kelly should get packets with 2, 4, 5 and 7 crayons.

Is what Mrs O'Neill thinks correct?

Explain why to a friend.

Investigate different ways of sharing the crayons equally between Dean and Kelly.

2. Four Missing Digits

Hannah has 9 digit cards.

| 0 | 2 | 3 | 4 | 5 | 6 | 7 | 8 | 9 |

She does not have a 1 digit card.

She uses 4 of her digit cards to complete this division.

1 [ ] ÷ [ ] = [ ] R [ ]

This is what Hannah did.

1 9 ÷ 5 = 3 R 4

Make a copy of what Hannah did.

Is what she did correct?

Explain why to a friend.

Investigate other ways Hannah could complete the division.

1. The picture instructions for making a sandwich are below, but they are in the wrong order. Redraw (and label) the pictures in your copy in the order you think they should be.

2. What times do these clocks show? Write the answer in digital form in your copy.

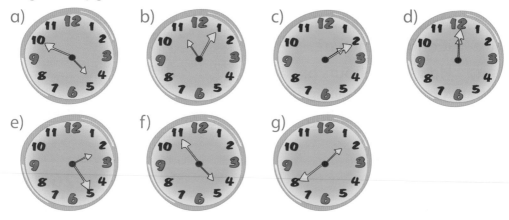

a)   b)   c)   d)

e)   f)   g)

3. Draw clocks in your copy to show the following times. Don't forget that your hour hand must be shorter than your minute hand.

   a) 2:20   b) 1:15   c) 7:45   d) 3:30

   e) 9:00   f) 10:50   g) 6:35

4. Draw a clock in your copy to show the time of each event.
   a) This is the time that I usually have my dinner.
   b) This is the time that I usually wake up on Saturdays.
   c) This is the time that I go to bed on a school night.

5. Answer these questions based on the TV guide above.

a) At what time do the programmes begin in the morning?

b) At what time is True Jackson VP: Max Mannequin shown?

c) At what time is Kung Fu Panda: Legends: Owl Be Back shown?

d) When is Rugrats shown?

e) How many episodes of iCarly are shown?

f) How many hours of iCarly are shown in total over the whole day?

Nickelodeon

06:00	iCarly: iFix a Popstar
06:30	iCarly: iSaved Your Life
07:00	SpongeBob SquarePants
07:30	SpongeBob SquarePants
08:00	Kung Fu Panda: Legends: Owl Be Back
08:30	SpongeBob SquarePants
09:00	Rugrats
09:30	Rugrats
10:00	Fairly Odd Parents
10:30	Fairly Odd Parents
11:00	iCarly: iFix a Popstar
11:30	iCarly: iSaved Your Life
12:00	SpongeBob SquarePants
18:30	Summer in Transylvania: The Date with Two Faces
19:00	Kung Fu Panda: Legends: Hometown Hero
19:30	iCarly: iSpace Out
20:00	Victorious: Trapped in an RV
20:30	Life With Boys: Social Death with Boys
21:00	True Jackson VP: Max Mannequin
21:30	iCarly: iBelieve in Bigfoot
22:00	SpongeBob SquarePants
22:30	SpongeBob SquarePants
23:00	iCarly: iEnrage Gibby
23:30	iCarly: iFind Lewbert's Lost Love
00:00	Teleshopping

Solve!   26. Time I

Netball Times

This clock shows when Ella's netball game starts.

This shows when Ella's netball game finishes.

How long does her game last?

Extension

When Ella gets home, her digital watch shows 12:00.

How long, in minutes, did it take Ella to get home after the game?

Strategy hints!

1. Look for the important words in the question.
2. Use a drawing.

1. A School Day

Children in the 3rd class at St Luke's Primary School
spend 5 hours on a school day with their teacher.

School starts at 9 o'clock.

School ends at 3:45pm.

Each break time and lunchtime starts on the hour
or 15, 30 or 45 minutes past the hour.

Morning break lasts 15 minutes.

Lunchtime lasts 1 hour 15 minutes.

Afternoon break lasts 15 minutes.

> Investigate how the
> teacher of the 3rd class
> might plan the school day.

2. A Coach Timetable

Eimear gets the coach from Delf to Eves and then
to Frume.

Each part of the
journey takes
over 4 hours.

Delf	0		:		
Eves	1		:		
Frume	1		:		

Eimear makes a
timetable of her journey.

She uses these 9 digits to complete her timetable.

This is what she did.

Could this
timetable be
correct?

Explain why
to a friend.

Delf	0	8	:	3	5
Eves	1	0	:	6	4
Frume	1	2	:	1	9

> Investigate other ways
> of completing the
> timetable.

1. Draw a horizontal line in your copy.

2. Draw a vertical line in your copy.

3. Draw parallel lines in your copy.

4. How many vertical lines are in each shape?

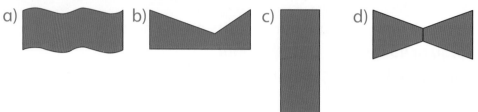

a)   b)   c)   d)

5. How many horizontal lines are in each shape?

a)   b)   c)   d)

6. List 5 things that you can find in your bedroom with these types of lines.
   a) Horizontal line (e.g. window ledge)
   b) Vertical line   c) Parallel lines

7. Use a ruler to draw the following angles in your copy.
   a) Less than a right angle
   b) A right angle   c) Greater than a right angle

8. Make a paper right angle and use it to measure the following angles. Write whether each angle is more than a right angle, less than a right angle or a right angle.

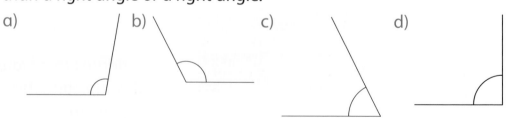

a)   b)   c)   d)

9. Stand up with your 2 arms pointing forwards and face the whiteboard. Follow these instructions.

    a) Rotate 2 right angles, anti-clockwise.
    b) Rotate a little bit less than 1 right angle, clockwise.
    c) Rotate a little bit more than 1 right angle, anti-clockwise.
    d) Rotate 1 right angle, anti-clockwise.
    e) Rotate 1 right angle, clockwise.
    f) Rotate a little bit more than 1 right angle, clockwise.
    g) Rotate a little bit less than 1 right angle, anti-clockwise.
    h) Finally, make 1 full rotation clockwise.
    i) Which way are you facing now?

Solve!   28. Lines and Angles

Arrowheads

a) What comes 5th in this pattern?

b) What comes 7th in this pattern?

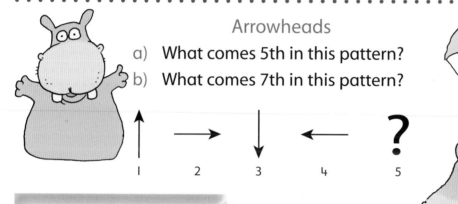

Extension

a) What comes 13th in this pattern?

b) What comes 20th in this pattern?

Strategy hints!

1. Look for the important words in the question.
2. Look for a pattern.
3. Use a drawing.

1. Luke's Lines

Luke has some 3x3 dotty grids.

He draws 3 types of line on different dotty grids.

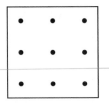

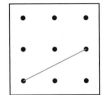 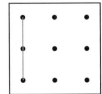

Make a copy of Luke's lines.

Luke says, 'I line is horizontal, another is vertical and the other is sloping.'

Which line is which?

Explain to a friend how you decided.

> Investigate horizontal, vertical and sloping lines on 3x3 dotty grids.

2. Ellen's Shapes

Ellen has 5 shapes.

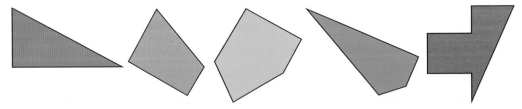

Put a cross in each right angle in a shape.

Explain to a friend how you decided.

How many right angles does each shape have?

Explain to your friend how you did this.

> Investigate right angles in shapes.

1. Find 3 things in your classroom that weigh less than 1 kg each. Write their names and weights in a table in your copy.

Name	Weight in Grams

2. Find 3 things in your classroom that weigh more than 1 kg each. Write their names and weights in a table in your copy.

3. Write the 6 items that you found in your classroom in order, from lightest to heaviest.

4. a) First estimate the weights of the following items in your classroom and then weigh them. Write your answers in your copy.

Item	Estimated Weight	Actual Weight	Difference
Milk/drink			
8 library books			
Pair of shoes			
Mobile phone			
Pile of copies			

    b) Were your estimates for the above items close to their actual weights? Work out the differences between your estimates and the actual weights and write down the differences in your copy. Remember, the smaller the difference, the better you are at estimating!

5. Use weighing scales to work out the answers to the following questions in your copy.

    a) What do the pair of shoes and the drink weigh together? Write your answers in your copy.

    > Pair of shoes = _____
    >
    > Drink = _____
    >
    > Total weight = _____

b) What do the mobile phone and the pile of copies weigh altogether? Write your answers in your copy.

Mobile phone = _____
Pile of copies = _____
Total weight = _____

c) How much heavier than the mobile phone are the 8 library books? Write your answers in your copy.

8 library books = _____
Mobile phone = _____
Answer = _____

d) What is the difference in weight between the pile of copies and the pair of shoes? Write your answers in your copy.

Weight of the pair of shoes = _____
Weight of the pile of copies = _____
Difference = _____

Solve!

Paints and Paintbrushes

What is the least number of paintbrushes it would take to tip the paintbrush side of this scales lower than the side with 4 tubes of paint?

Extension

How many paintbrushes weigh the same as 7 tubes of paint?

Strategy hints!

1. Look for the important words in the question.
2. Use a drawing.
3. Think logically.

1. Pieces of Fruit

Jon has 3 pieces of fruit.

He uses only a balance to find which piece of fruit is the heaviest.

Jon says, I found that the apple was the heaviest.

Explain to a friend how Jon might have done this.

Investigate finding the heaviest of 4, 5, 6, etc. pieces of fruit using a balance.

2. Peanut Butter

3 children each have a partly filled jar of peanut butter.

Each jar holds a maximum of 150g.

The number of grams in each jar is in the 10 times table.

Andrew   Mary   Clar

Mary's jar has 20g more peanut butter than Andrew's jar.

Andrew's jar has 60g less peanut butter than Clar's jar.

Mary says, 'I have 30g, Clar has 70g and Andrew has 10g.'

Could what Mary said be true?

Explain to a friend how you decided.

Investigate what amount of peanut butter could be in each jar.

1. a) $562 + 23$ b) $154 - 27$ c) $521 - 209$ d) $364 + 257$

2. Work out the answers in your copy.

   a) $381 + \boxed{} = 460$ b) $750 - \boxed{} = 154$

3. Work out the following number sentences and then write the answers in your copy.

   a) $65 + \boxed{} = 82$ b) $16 + \boxed{} = 274$

   c) $48 - \boxed{} = 11$ d) $119 - \boxed{} = 62$

   e) $351 - \boxed{} = 205$ f) $460 + \boxed{} = 608$

   g) $775 + \boxed{} = 981$ h) $480 - \boxed{} = 349$

4. Write number sentences for each of these word problems and then work out the answers.

   a) There were 461 children in Dara's school last year. If the number of children rose by 17 this year, how many children are in the school now?

   b) There are 156 apartments in the Botanic Heights apartment complex. 29 of them are 1-bed apartments and the rest are 2-bed apartments. How many 2-bed apartments are there?

5. Make up your own word problems for these number sentences. Write them in your copy and then work out the answers.

   a) $377 + 408 = \boxed{}$ b) $415 - 120 = \boxed{}$

Missing Number

Find the missing number in this sum.

$5 + 5 + 8 + ? + 6 + 4 = 30$

Extension

Use the same pattern to find the missing numbers in this sum.

$9 + ? + 2 + ? = 20$

Strategy hints!

1. Look for the important words in the question.
2. Look for a pattern.

1. An Adventure Playground

Gráinne visits an adventure playground.

Gráinne writes a problem about her visit:

57 children from St Stephen's School visit the playground. 28 of them are in 3rd class. How many are not in 3rd class?

Write the number sentence for the problem.

Work out the answer.

> Investigate writing maths problems about a visit to an adventure playground.

2. The School Fair

Oisín helps on a stall at his school's fair.

Oisín writes a problem about the school fair:

207 adults and 360 children go to the school fair. Altogether, how many go to the school fair?

Write the number sentence for the problem.

Work out the answer.

> Investigate writing maths problems about a school fair.

1. Conduct a survey among 12 of your classmates to find out each person's favourite item of clothing from the choices below. Put the information into a table like this one in your copy. (Remember, each person can only vote once.)

Favourite Types of Clothes to Wear

Jeans	Dress	Suit	Tracksuit	Shoes	T-shirt

2. Now make a pictogram in your copy to represent the data that you have collected. Remember to label your pictogram.

3. Make a block graph in your copy to represent your data. Remember to label your block graph.

4. Make a bar chart in your copy to represent your data. (Always use a ruler when making graphs!) Remember to label your bar chart.

5. Answer the following questions based on your data.
   a) How many people chose jeans?
   b) How many people chose a dress?
   c) How many people chose a suit?
   d) How many people chose a tracksuit?
   e) How many people chose shoes?
   f) How many people chose a T-shirt?
   g) What type of clothing did most people choose?
   h) What type of clothing did the fewest people choose?
   i) If you carried out this same survey on 12 teachers rather than on 12 pupils, do you think the results might be different? Explain.

Car Colours

Here are the colours of 3 teachers' cars.

	Green	Black	White
Mr Green		✔	
Mr White			✔
Mr Black	✔		

a) Which teacher has a car that is the same colour as his name?

b) All the teachers want to drive cars that are the same colour as their name. Who will have to drive Mr Green's car?

Strategy hints!

1. Look for the important words in the question.
2. Use a table or a chart.
3. Think logically.

Extension

Three children each own a pet. The pets are a fish, a bird and a dog.

Daisy's pet has more legs than Amy's pet. Brad's pet has no legs at all.

Who owns which pet?

1. Jade's Block Graph

Jade draws a block graph.

She forgets to give the graph

a) a title

b) the names of the 2 axes

c) the scale on each axis.

Darragh completes the missing information.

Make a copy of what Darragh did.

Could what Darragh did be correct?

Explain why to a friend.

> Investigate different ways of completing Jade's block graph.

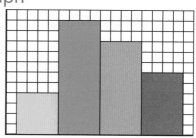

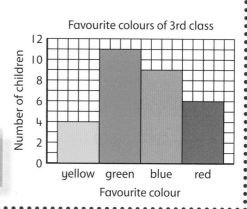

Favourite colours of 3rd class

2. 2 Times Table Digits

Áine looks at the 2 times table numbers.

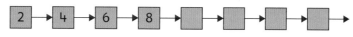

Extend Áine's sequence of numbers.

Explain how you did this to a friend.

Áine counts the number of times each digit appears in her sequence up to 20 times 2.

She starts to make a table of the frequencies.

Digit	0	1	2	3	4	5	6	7	8	9
Frequency to 20 times 2	4	5	9	5	5					

Is what Áine did correct?

Explain to your friend how you decided.

Complete the table for Áine.

Explain to your friend how you did it.

> Investigate digits in the 2 times table numbers.

1. See if you can write out the poem '30 Days Has September' in your copy without looking back at where it is written in your book.

2. Look at the calendar at the beginning of this chapter, on page 196, in your Pupil's Book.
   a) How many days are in May?
   b) How many days are in September?
   c) How many days are in April?
   d) How many days are in August?
   e) According to the calendar, what day is 10 March?
   f) According to the calendar, what day is 6 June?
   g) According to the calendar, what day is 25 May?
   h) How many months are in a season?
   i) How many seasons are in a year?
   j) How many days are there from 1 January until 17 February?
   k) How many full weeks are there from 24 July until 10 November?
   l) If you started saving up your pocket money on 17 August and saved until 11 December, for how many full months, weeks and days would you have saved?

3. Try these. Use your maths copy to work out the answers if necessary. Write your answers in your copy.
   a) 1 hr 20 mins = _____ mins
   b) 2 hrs 2 mins = _____ mins
   c) 1 hr 26 mins = _____ mins
   d) 2 hrs 31 mins = _____ mins
   e) 2 hrs 42 mins = _____ mins
   f) 3 hrs 36 mins = _____ mins
   g) $4\frac{1}{2}$ hrs = _____ hrs _____ mins = _____ mins
   h) $2\frac{1}{4}$ hrs = _____ hrs _____ mins = _____ mins

4. Try these. Write your answers in your copy.

    a) 90 mins = _____ hr _____ mins = $1\frac{1}{2}$ hrs

    b) 210 mins = _____ hrs _____ mins = _____

    c) 15 mins = _____ hr

    d) 105 mins = _____ hr _____ mins = _____ hrs

    e) 72 mins = _____ hr _____ mins

    f) 194 mins = _____ hrs _____ mins

    g) 216 mins = _____ hrs _____ mins

    h) 199 mins = _____ hrs _____ mins

    i) 218 mins = _____ hrs _____ mins

    j) 547 mins = _____ hrs _____ mins

Solve!   32. Time 2

Karate Training

The calendar shows part of a month and the days
that Weng trains for karate.

S	M	T	W	T	F	S
				1	2	3
4	K	6	7	8	9	K
11	12	13	14	K	16	17
18	19	K	21	22	23	

What are the next 2 dates in this
month that Weng will train?

Strategy hints!

1. Look for the important
    words in the question.

2. Use a table or a chart.

Extension

How can you tell that this month is not February?

1. Minutes and Hours

Robert has 10 digit cards.

| 0 | 1 | 2 | 3 | 4 | 5 | 6 | 7 | 8 | 9 |

He uses 4 of the digit cards to complete this missing digits statement.

☐ hours ☐ 5 minutes = ☐ ☐ 5 minutes

This is what Robert did.

2 hours 4 5 minutes = 1 6 5 minutes

Copy Robert's statement.

Which 4 digits did Robert use?

Is what Robert did correct?

Explain why to a friend.

> Investigate different ways of completing Robert's statement.

2. Mondays and Fridays

Orla looks at the month of January in calendars for past years.

January	Year: _____				
Monday					
Tuesday					
Wednesday					
Thursday					
Friday					
Saturday					
Sunday					

She notices that there are some years when there are 4 Mondays and 4 Fridays in January and some years when there are not.

> Investigate the number of Mondays and Fridays in the month of January in different years.

1. Write the names of these 3-D shapes in your copy.

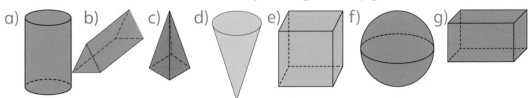

a)   b)   c)   d)   e)   f)   g)

2. In your copy, write the name of a 3-D shape that:
   a) Can roll
   b) Has 12 edges
   c) Has 4 faces
   d) Can stack
   e) Has 8 edges
   f) Has 5 faces
   g) Can slide
   h) Has 6 faces
   i) Has 5 corners
   j) Has 6 corners
   k) Can stack and roll
   l) Can roll but cannot stack

3. Can you find objects in your classroom that use the following 3-D shapes? Copy this table and fill it in.

	Cube	Cuboid	Triangular prism	Pyramid	Cylinder	Sphere	Cone
Name of your object							
Draw your object							

4. Write the name of the 3-D shape that matches each net.

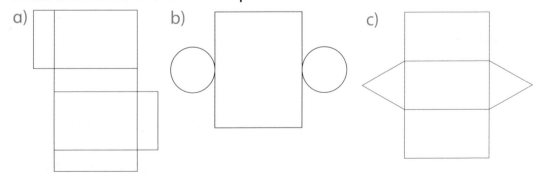

a)   b)   c)

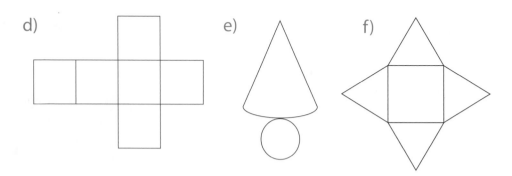

d)   e)   f)

5.   Complete the following sentences in your copy.

     a)   A square can be found on the net of a _____.

     b)   A circle can be found on the net of a _____.

     c)   A triangle can be found on the net of a _____.

     d)   A rectangle can be found on the net of a _____.

Solve!   33. 3-D Shapes

Corners, Edges, Faces

Get 2 connecting blocks and clip them together.

Look at the shape you have made. Does it have more corners, more edges or more faces?

Remember, count the face with the connector as 1 face.

Strategy hints!

1.   Look for the important words in the question.

2.   Make a model.

Extension

Clip 2 more connecting blocks on top of this shape.

Count the corners, edges and faces.

What do you notice?

1. Rolling

Niall has a collection of 3-D shapes.

Niall says, 'Some of my shapes will roll and others will not roll.'

Make a prediction about what Niall says for each of his shapes.

Explain reasons for your predictions to a friend.

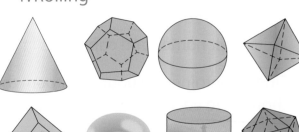

Investigate rolling 3-D shapes.

2. Straw Cuboids

Dylan has lots of 7cm and 10cm straws and balls of play dough.

7 cm

10 cm

He makes a cuboid with the straws and balls.

Make Dylan's cuboid.

Make a drawing of Dylan's cuboid.

How many 7cm straws did you use?

How many 10cm straws did you use?

What is the total number of straws used for the cuboid?

How many balls did you use?

Explain to a friend how you worked it out.

Investigate making different cuboids with the straws.

1. Find 3 containers in your classroom that have a capacity of less than 1 litre each.
   Write their names and capacities in your copy.

2. Find 3 containers in your classroom that have a capacity of more than 1 litre each. Write their names and capacities in your copy.

3. List the 6 containers that you found in your classroom in order, from smallest to largest capacity.

4. Make this table in your copy.
   a) Find any 5 containers that you have not measured the capacity of yet and name them in the table in your copy.
   b) Estimate each container's capacity.
   c) Use a measuring jug to measure each container's correct capacity.
   d) Finally, work out the differences between each of your estimates and the actual capacities.

Container	Estimated Capacity	Actual Capacity	Difference

5. Look at your table. If you filled each of the first 2 containers with water and poured them both into a measuring jug together, how much water would be in the measuring jug in total? First work out your answer in your copy and then check it by trying it out!

6. If you filled each of the last 2 containers in your table with water and poured them both into a measuring jug together, how much water would be in the measuring jug in total? First work out your answer in your copy and then check it by trying it out!

7. If you filled your largest container with water and then carefully scooped out enough water to fill your smallest container, how much water would be left in the large container? First work out your answer in your copy and then check it by trying it out!

8. If you filled your second largest container with water and then carefully scooped out enough water to fill your second smallest container, how much water would be left in the large container? First work out your answer in your copy and then check it by trying it out!

Solve!   34. Capacity

Equal Glasses

Ruby pours juice into 3 glasses.
She wants to make all the glasses equal.

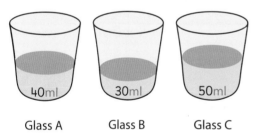

| 40ml | 30ml | 50ml |
| Glass A | Glass B | Glass C |

What must Ruby do to make them equal?

Strategy hints!

1. Look for the important words in the question.
2. Use a drawing.
3. Think logically.

Extension

If Ruby wanted to pour all the juice into just 2 equal glasses, how much would be in each glass?

1.4 Containers and a Jug

Emily has a 1l, 3l, 9l and 12l container and a very large jug.

Emily fills the 1l, the 9l and the 12l containers and pours each into the jug.

She records what she did in her table.

1l	3l	9l	12l	Total number of litres	Number of jugs used
1		1	1		

Complete the table.

Explain to a friend how the table works and how you worked out the total.

> Investigate making different amounts using one or more containers.

2. Glasses of Lemonade

James has 15 glasses, some with lemonade and some empty.

5 x 1000ml   5 x 500ml   5 x 0ml

James shares the lemonade equally among Aaron, Daniel and Katie.

Each has 5 glasses and the same amount of lemonade.

No lemonade is moved from glass to glass.

This is what James did.

Aaron	Daniel	Katie

Draw what James did.

How many ml does each child have?

> Investigate other ways James could do the sharing.